No.1 Hits of the 80s

Wise Publications
London/New York/Sydney/Paris/Copenhagen/Madrid/Tokyo

CW00541277

Exclusive distributors:
Music Sales Limited
8/9 Frith Street,
London W1V 5TZ, England.

Music Sales Pty Limited
120 Rothschild Avenue
Rosebery, NSW 2018,
Australia.

Order No.AM956582
ISBN 0-7119-8171-X
This book © Copyright 2000 by Wise Publications

Book design by Paula Snell Design
Music arranged by Derek Jones
Music engraved by Paul Ewers Music Design
Compiled by Nick Crispin

Photographs courtesy of London Features

Printed in the United Kingdom by
Redwood Books Limited, Trowbridge, Wiltshire.

Your Guarantee of Quality
As publishers, we strive to produce every book to
the highest commercial standards. The book has
been carefully designed to minimise awkward page
turns and to make playing from it a real pleasure.
Particular care has been given to specifying
acid-free, neutral-sized paper made from pulps
which have not been elemental chlorine bleached.
This pulp is from farmed sustainable forests
and was produced with special regard for the
environment. Throughout, the printing and binding
have been planned to ensure a sturdy, attractive
publication which should give years of enjoyment.
If your copy fails to meet our high standards,
please inform us and we will gladly replace it.

Music Sales' complete catalogue describes
thousands of titles and is available in full colour
sections by subject, direct from Music Sales
Limited. Please state your areas of interest and
send a cheque/postal order for £1.50 for postage
to: Music Sales Limited, Newmarket Road,
Bury St. Edmunds, Suffolk IP33 3YB.

www.musicsales.com

Atomic

Words & Music by Deborah Harry & Jimmy Destri

Oh   your hair is   beau - ti - ful,

oh _____ to - night. _____ A - to - mic.

All Around The World

Words & Music by Lisa Stansfield, Ian Devaney & Andrew Morris

I don't know where my baby is but I'll find him somewhere somehow. I've got to let him know how much I care. I'll never give up looking for my baby.

Been a-round the world and I I I I can't find my ba - by.

I don't know when I don't know why, why he's gone a-way and I

don't know where he can be, my ba - by, but I'm gon-na find him.

Mm mm.

Strings

repeat chorus

Verse 2:
So open hearted, he never did me wrong
I was the one, the weakest one of all,
And now I'm oh so sad
I don't think he's coming back.

I did too much lying *etc.*

Chain Reaction

Words & Music by Barry Gibb, Robin Gibb & Maurice Gibb

1. You took a mys-te-ry and made me_____ want it.
(Verse 2 see block lyric)

You got a pe-des-tal and put me on it. You made me love you out of

feel-ing no-thing. Some-thing___ that you do.___ Oh!

And I was there not dan-cing with a - ny - one.

You took a lit-tle then you took me___ ov-er.___ You set your mark on

steal-ing my heart— a-way. Cry-ing, try-ing a — ny-thing for you.—

I'm in the mid-dle of a chain re — ac — tion.—

You give me all the af-ter mid-night ac-tion, I, I wan-na get you where

I can let you make all that love to me.—

love, love, love.___ We talk a - bout___ love.___

Let me hold you for the fisrt ex - plo - sion,

arms___ will___ cov - er you. All___ you got - ta do.___

Verse 2:
You make me tremble when your hand goes lower
You taste a little then you swallow slower
Nature has a way of yielding treasure
Pleasure made for you
You gotta plan, your future is on the run
Shine a light for the whole world over
You never find the love if you hide away
Crying, dying
All you gotta do is.

Get in the middle of a chain reaction
You get a medal when you're lost in action
I'm gonna get your love all ready for
The sweet sensation
Instant radiation
You let me hold you for the first explosion
We get a picture of our love in motion
My arms will cover, my lips smother you
No more left to say
We talk about love, love, love
We talk about love.

Do You Really Want To Hurt Me

Words & Music by George O'Dowd, Jonathan Moss, Roy Hay & Michael Craig

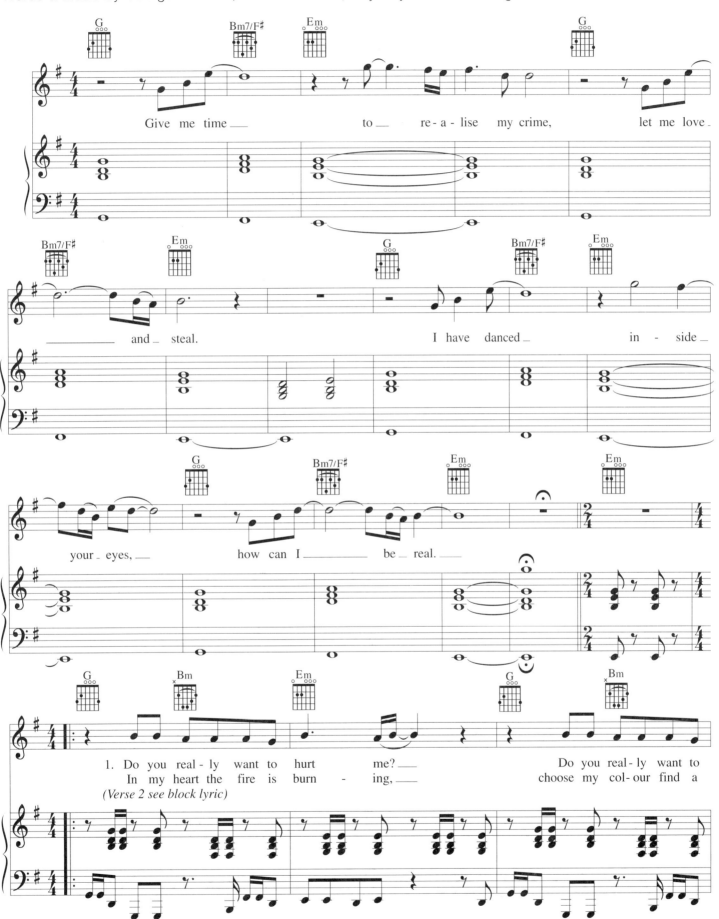

Do you real - ly want to make me ___ cry?

If it's ___ love ___ you ___

want from me, ___ then take it ___ a- way, ___ ev - 'ry - thing's ___ not ___

Coda

D.%.al Coda

what you ___ see, ___ it's ov - er ___ a - gain. ___

Verse 2:
Words are few
I have spoken
I could waste a thousand years
Wrapped in sorrow, words are token
Come inside and catch my tears
You've been talking but believe me
If it's true you do not know
This boy loves without a reason
I'm prepared to let you go.

23

China In Your Hand

Words & Music by Carol Decker & Ronald Rogers

It was a flight on the wings of a young girl's dreams___ that

flew too far a - way.___

Don't push___ too far, your dreams___ are chi - na in your hand.___

Don't wish___ too hard be - cause___ they may come true___ and you can't help___ them.

You don't know what you might have set up - on your - self.

Chi - na in your hand.

In your hand, your hand.

Saxophone

Verse 2:
Come from greed, never born o' the seed.
Took a life from a barren land
Oh, eyes wide like a child in the form of man
A phophecy for a fantasy
The curse of a vivid man.

Don't push too far *etc.*

Every Little Thing She Does Is Magic

Words & Music by Sting

1. Though I've tried be-fore___ to tell___ her of the feel-ings I have for her in___ my _____ heart _____

ev-ery-time ___ that I ___ come near ___ her I just lose ___

___ my nerve ___ as I've ___ done from the start. ___

Chorus

Eve-ry lit-tle thing she does ___ is ma-gic ev-ery-thing she

do just turns ___ me on ___ ev-en though my life be-fore ___ was tra-gic now I know my

love for her — goes on. ____

2. Do I ____

I re-solved to call ____ her up

a thou-sand ____ times a day

and ask her if she'll mar-ry me

30

Verse 2:
Do I have to tell the story
Of a thousand rainy days since we first met
It's a big enough umbrella
But it's always me that ends up getting wet.
Chorus: (Repeat)

Ghost Town

Words & Music by Jerry Dammers

34

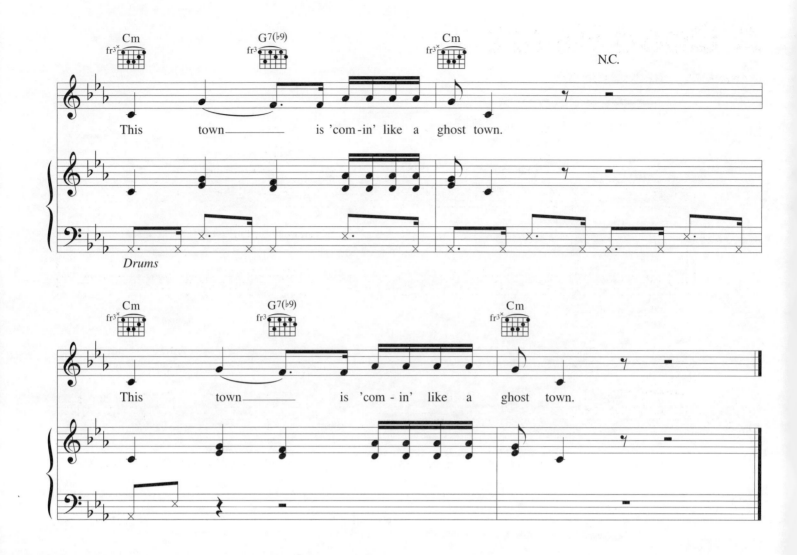

Verse 2:
This town is 'comin' like a ghost town
Why must the youth fight against themself
Government's leavin' the youths on the shelf
This place is 'comin' like a ghost town
No job to be found in this country
Can't go on no more
The people gettin' angry.

La la la la *etc.*

A Good Heart

Words & Music by Maria McKee

Verse 2 My expectations may be high, I blame that on my youth,
Soon enough I'll learn the fateful truth.
I'll face it like a fighter, then boast of how I've grown
Anything is better than being alone.
Well I know 'cause I learn a little every day,
I know 'cause I listen when the experts say

Chorus That a . . . .

Verse 3 As I reflect on all my childhood dreams
My ideas of love weren't as foolish as they seemed
If I don't start looking now then I'll be left behind,
And a good heart these days, it's hard to find.
I know it's a dream I'm willing to defend
I know it will all be worth it in the end.

I Knew You Were Waiting (For Me)

Words & Music by Simon Climie & Dennis Morgan

VERSE 2:
With an endless desire
I kept on searching
Sure in time our eyes would meet.

And like the bridge is on fire
The hurt is over
One touch and you set me free.

I don't regret a single moment no I don't, looking back
When I think of all those disappointments, I just laugh, I just laugh.

Move Closer

Words & Music by Phyllis Nelson

Verse 2:
So when I say "Sugar",
And I whisper "I love you",
Well, I know you're gonna answer in the sweetest voice,
Saying "My sexy baby, I love you too".
There's much room for passion,
There's no room for fears.
When good love flows smoothly between us,
My dear, ooh, why don't you
Move closer *etc.*

Jealous Guy

Words & Music by John Lennon

1. I was dream-ing of the past _____
2. I was feel-ing in - se - cure _____
3. (Whistle) .... *etc.*
4. I was trying to catch your eyes _____

and my heart _ was beat-ing _ fast _____
you might not love _ me a - ny - more _____
thought that you _ were trying to hide _____

I be-gan _ to lose _ con-trol _
I was shiv - er - ing _ in - side _
I was swal - low-ing _ my pain.

I be - gan _____ to lose _ con-trol
I was shiv - er - ing _ in - side
I was swal - low-ing _ my pain

Perfect

Words & Music by Mark E. Nevin

(Verses 2 & 3 see block lyrics)

Too— ma-ny peo-ple take sec-ond best,_____ well I won't take a-ny-thing less.___ It's got to be,_____ yeah,___ per - - - - - - fect. 2. Young_____ hearts are

1. To Coda ⊕ N.C.

2. -fect. Guitar

3. Young___ hearts are

Verses 2 & 3:
Young hearts are foolish
They make such mistakes
They're much too eager
To give their love away
Well I have been foolish
Too many times
Now I'm determined
I'm gonna get it right.

It's got to be perfect *etc.*

Take My Breath Away

Words by Tom Whitlock
Music by Giorgio Moroder

Take my breath a - way."

"Take my breath a -

D.S. al Coda

My   love, ___   take my breath a - way.

My   love, ___   take my breath a -

Repeat and Fade

There Must Be An Angel
(Playing With My Heart)

Words & Music by Annie Lennox & David A. Stewart

D.S. to Fade on Chorus

VERSE 2:

No one on earth could feel like this
I'm thrown and over blown with bliss
There must be an angel
Playing with my heart.
And when I think that I'm alone
It seems there's more of us at home
It's a multitude of angels
And they're playing with my heart.

Town Called Malice

Words & Music by Paul Weller

stop dream-ing of the qui-et life— coz it's the one we'll nev-er know.— And
(Verses 2 & 3 see block lyrics)

big de-ci-sion in a town called Ma-lice._____

Ooh,_____

yeah._____

D.%. al Coda

Ooh._____

Ma - lice.   Yeah.

Repeat to fade

In   a   town   called

Verse 2:
Rows and rows of disused milk-floats
Stand dying in the dairy yard
And a hundred lonely housewifes
Clutch empty milk bottles to their hearts
Hanging out their old love letters
On the line to dry
It's enough to make you stop believing
When tears come fast and furious.

In a town called Malice.

Verse 3:
The ghost of a steam train
Echoes down my track
It's at the moment bound for nowhere
Just going 'round and 'round
Oh playground kids and creaking swings
Lost laughter in the breeze
I could go on for hours and I probably will
But I'd sooner put some joy back

In this town called Malice.

When The Going Gets Tough, The Tough Get Going

Words & Music by Wayne Brathwaite, Barry Eastmond, Robert John Lange & Billy Ocean

touch— you?— (Can I touch you?) And do the things that lov - ers do.—

(Can I touch you?) Ooh— (ooh—) wan-na hold— you.— (Wan-na hold you) I

got - ta get it through to you.— Oh,— cos when the

go-ing gets tough,— (go - ing gets tough)(when the go - ing gets rough,— oh.— (Go-

Verse 3:
I'm gonna buy me a one-way ticket
Nothing's gonna hold me back
Your love's like a soul train coming
And I feel it coming down the track.

(Darling) I'll climb any mountain *etc.*

True Blue

Words & Music by Madonna Ciccone & Steve Bray

Hey! (Wait!)

Lis - ten.

But no mat - ter where I go you're the one for me, ba - by,

this I know. Coz it's true love, you're the one I'm

dream - in' of. Your heart fits me like a glove

and I'm gon - na be too blue, ba - by, I love you.

Verse 2:
I've heard all the lines
I've cracked, oh, so many times
Those teardrops, they won't fall again
I'm so excited coz you're my best friend
So if you should ever doubt
Wonder what love is all about
Just think back and remember dear
Those words whispered in your ear.

I said true love *etc.*

84

The Winner Takes It All

Words & Music by Benny Andersson & Björn Ulvaeus

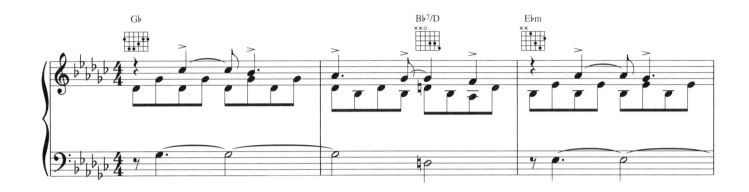

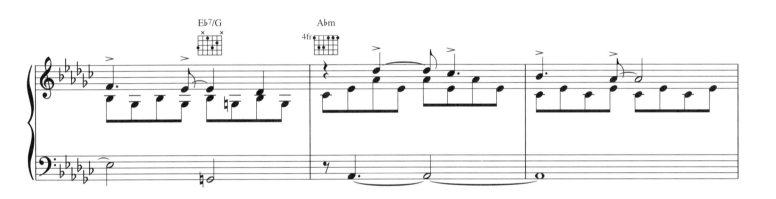

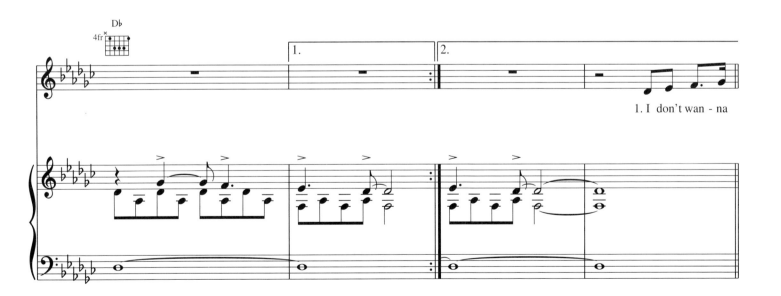

1. I don't wan - na

1. talk   a - bout things we've gone through,   though it's hurt-ing
2. arms   think-ing I be -longed there,   I fi - gured it made
3. kiss   like I used to kiss you,   does it feel the
4. talk   if it makes you feel sad,   and I un-der-

me,   now it's his - to - ry.   I've played all my
sense,   build-ing me a fence,   build - ing me a
same   when she calls your name?   Some-where deep in -
- stand   you've come to shake my hand.   I a - po - lo -

cards   and that's what you've done too,   no-thing more to
home,   think-ing I'd be strong there,   but I was a
- side,   you must know I miss you,   but what can I
- gize   if it makes you feel bad   see-ing me so

The win-ner takes it

all.

You Win Again

Words & Music by Barry Gibb, Robin Gibb & Maurice Gibb

I could-n't fig-ure why you could-n't give me what ev-'ry-bo-dy needs,—

I'm gon-na break down your de-fen-ces one by____ one.____

I'm gon-na hit you from all sides____ lay your for-tress op-en____

wide,____ no-bo-dy stops this bo-dy from ta-kin' you. You bet-ter be

D.%. al Coda

Coda

Repeat to fade

96